Key Stage 2
English Practice Papers

Carol Matchett

Write your name and school below before you start the practice papers.

First name	
Last name	
School	

After you have finished each paper and had it marked, write your test score in these boxes.

Reading Paper	
Grammar, Punctuation and Spelling Paper 1	
Grammar, Punctuation and Spelling Paper 2	
Total	

Schofield&Sims

Contents

> **Note for adults helping with Grammar, Punctuation and Spelling**
> The script for Grammar, Punctuation and Spelling Paper 2 should be removed from the book before the child starts the test.

General instructions

This book contains the following three practice papers.

- Reading Paper (1 hour)
- Grammar, Punctuation and Spelling Paper 1: questions (45 minutes)
- Grammar, Punctuation and Spelling Paper 2: spelling (15 minutes)

It is best to do the papers in the order they appear in the book, but don't do all the tests at the same time. Have a break between tests.

Before you start a test

When you are ready to do one of the practice papers, find a quiet place where you can concentrate.

Make sure you have enough time to complete the practice paper before you start it. Apart from the spelling test (Grammar, Punctuation and Spelling Paper 2), all the tests in this book should be timed. Use a clock or a watch to check the time or ask an adult to time the test for you.

There is an instruction page before each test. This explains exactly what to do in the test. You can ask an adult to help you read this page and explain things to you. Make sure you understand what to do before you begin. Ask questions if you are not sure.

When you are ready to begin, turn to the first page of the practice paper and start timing the test.

During the test

Work through the test on your own.

The questions in Grammar, Punctuation and Spelling Paper 2 will be read out loud by the adult who is helping you.

Work through all the questions, thinking carefully. Try your best to answer them all. If you can't answer a question, move to the next one. You can come back to it later.

Read the questions carefully and check your answers so you don't make careless mistakes.

Don't look at the answers before or during the test.

After the test

Ask an adult to mark your practice paper using the answers and mark scheme on pages 39–49. Record your score in the boxes on pages 3, 50 and 51.

Look at any questions you couldn't do or answered incorrectly. These are topics you need to revise. The Schofield & Sims **Key Stage 2 English Revision Guide** will help you with this.

Instructions for the Reading test

For the Reading test, you will need the separate Reading Booklet. The Reading Booklet is an eight-page pull-out section found in the centre of this book. Before you begin the test, ask an adult to pull the booklet out.

Instructions for the Reading Paper

You have one hour to read the selection of texts in the Reading Booklet and answer the questions about them. Read one text and answer the questions about that text before moving on to read the next text. You will find there are four texts and four sets of questions in this practice paper.

Questions and answers

There are different types of question for you to answer in different ways. There is always a space for your answer and this shows you what type of answer is needed.

- Some questions are followed by a short line. This shows that you need only write a word or a few words in your answer.
- Some questions are followed by a few lines. This gives you space to write more words or a sentence or two.
- Some questions are followed by a number of lines. This shows that you need to give a longer, more detailed answer to explain your opinion.
- For some questions, you do not need to write anything at all – you just need to tick, draw lines to, or put a ring around your answer. Always read the instructions on these questions carefully so that you know how to answer the question.

Marks

The numbers in the right-hand margin of the page tell you how many marks each question is worth.

Work through the questions until your time is up. Refer to the Reading Booklet when you need to. Sometimes a question includes a page reference and you should always refer to the text on that page to help you answer it.

Try to answer all of the questions. If you can't answer a question, move on and return to it later, if you have time. Remember that you should keep referring back to your Reading Booklet.

You are now ready to start the test. Make sure you have the separate Reading Booklet before you begin. Remember, you have **one hour** to read the texts in the Reading Booklet and answer the questions.

Reading Paper

Questions 1–7 are about the poem
'There will come soft rains' (page 2)

1 According to the first part of the poem what sounds will be heard? Give three sounds.

1. ....

2. ....

3. ....

1 mark

2 In the first verse of the poem, the poet uses words with an alliterative effect. How does this add to the mood of the poem?

....

....

1 mark

3 The focus of the poem changes at the start of verse 4. How does the focus change at this point?

....

....

1 mark

4 In the tenth line of the poem the word 'utterly' means:

Tick one.

silently. ☐

completely. ☐

perfectly. ☐

fearfully. ☐

1 mark

page 7
total

please turn over

5   The poem says, 'Spring ... would scarcely know that we were gone.'

Why would 'we' be gone?

....

....

1

6   What is the main message of the poem?

Tick **one**.

Mankind will destroy nature.   ☐

Nature will outlive the destruction of mankind.   ☐

Nature is beautiful but fragile.   ☐

Mankind should think more about nature.   ☐

1

7   The poem is called 'There will come soft rains'. Explain **two** things that the word 'soft' suggests about the rains in the poem.

....

....

....

2 m

Revision Guide links
If you need help after your test has been marked, read the following pages in the Revision Guide:
Question 5 page 19   Question 6 page 18
Question 7 page 20

Questions 8–13 are about the article
'The dodo' (pages 3–4)

8 Use the text to help you complete this table of facts about dodos.

Natural habitat	
Diet	
Nesting	
Size	

2 marks

9 Why is it impossible to know for sure exactly what a dodo looked like?
Give **two** reasons.

1. ....

2. ....

2 marks

10 How did the arrival of the sailors change the dodo's natural habitat?

....

....

1 mark

11 In 'What happened to the dodo?' the dodo is described as defenceless.
Use information from the text to explain why the dodo was easy prey.

....

....

....

....

....

2 marks

pages
8–9
total

please turn over

Revision Guide links
If you need help after your test has been marked,
read the following pages in the Revision Guide:
Question 8 page 27   Question 9 page 28
Question 10 page 27   Question 11 page 28

12 In the section 'An image problem', what does the word 'bizarre' tell us about the dodo's appearance?

....

1

13 Using information from the text, tick **one** box in each row to show whether each statement is true or false.

	True	False
The dodo only ever lived on the island of Mauritius.		
There is no scientific evidence that dodos existed.		
There are no records of dodos before 1598.		
Savery's painting of a dodo was entirely accurate.		

1

Questions 14–22 are about the information leaflet 'Tenbury Woods' (pages 5–6)

14 Look at the introduction to the leaflet. How can you tell that it is quiet in Tenbury Woods?

....

....

1 mark

15 Look at the visitor information. Not all visitors treat the woods with respect. Give **two** ways in which they might damage the woods.

1. ....

2. ....

1 mark

16 What is an 'ancient woodland'?

....

1 mark

17 Explain how cutting down trees has had a positive impact on wildlife in Tenbury Woods.

....

....

....

1 mark

18 Tick **one** box in each row to show whether each statement is a fact or an opinion.

	Fact	**Opinion**
A walk in the woods is always pleasant.		
The woods are close to the town of Tenbury.		
The woods are a Local Nature Reserve.		
The woods are special.		

1 mark

pages 10–11 total

please turn over

Revision Guide links
If you need help after your test has been marked, read the following pages in the Revision Guide:
Question 14 pages 28–29   Question 15 page 27
Question 16 pages 26–27   Question 17 page 28
Question 18 page 30

19 The Waterside Walk is described as 'suitable for all'. How does the information about the walk make it sound 'suitable for all'?

Give **two** ways.

1. ....

....

2. ....

....

2 m

20 According to the leaflet, what activities might you do on the Woodland Trail? Give **two** examples.

1. ....

2. ....

1 m

21 According to the leaflet, which is the best season for the following activities? Draw a line to match the season to the event.

spring	•	•	finding fungi
summer	•	•	dramatic photographs
autumn	•	•	seeing a kingfisher
winter	•	•	bird-watching

1 m

22 Look at the message from the woodland ranger. Explain how he feels about being the ranger at Tenbury Woods. Refer to the text to help you.

....

....

....

....

2 m

Revision Guide links
If you need help after your test has been marked, read the following pages in the Revision Guide:
Question 19 pages 28–29
Question 20 pages 26–27
Question 21 page 27
Question 22 page 31

Questions 23–36 are about
'The War of the Worlds' (pages 7–8)

23 Circle the correct option to complete each sentence below.

a) At the start of the extract, the crowd around the pit had...

| scattered. | grown. | decreased. | dispersed. |

1 mark

b) The people were elbowing and jostling one another...

| to get away. | to get out of the pit. | to get a better view. | to get a souvenir. |

1 mark

c) The astronomer, Ogilvy, was very...

| excited. | annoyed. | fearful. | pleased. |

1 mark

24 How did they know there was something inside?

....

1 mark

25 How did the narrator know that the cylinder lid had come off?

....

1 mark

pages
12–13
total

Revision Guide links
If you need help after your test has been marked,
read the following pages in the Revision Guide:
Question 23 pages 7–9   Question 24 page 7
Question 25 page 7

please turn over

Schofield & Sims • Key Stage 2 **English Practice Papers**   **13**

26 Look at the paragraph beginning 'I think everyone expected to see…'.

The word 'terrestrial' in this paragraph is closest in meaning to...

Tick **one**.

ordinary. ☐

continental. ☐

earthly, of earth. ☐

regular. ☐

1 m

27 Which part of the creature came out first?

....

1 m

28 The writer describes the movements of the creature as 'greyish billowy movements'. Find and copy **three** verbs in the paragraph that suggest similar movements.

1. ....

2. ....

3. ....

1 m

29 The mood of the crowd changes once they see what is inside the cylinder.

a) How does the mood of the crowd change at this point?

....

....

1 m

b) How was the narrator's reaction to the creature different to the rest of the crowd?

....

....

1 m

Revision Guide links

If you need help after your test has been marked, read the following pages in the Revision Guide:

Question 26 page 4   Question 27 page 8
Question 28 page 12   Question 29 page 17

30 In the paragraph beginning 'A big greyish rounded bulk…', the narrator uses comparisons to help describe the creature.

How do these comparisons help the reader understand what the creature looks like?

....

....

....

1 mark

31 In the paragraph beginning 'Two large dark-coloured eyes…', the writer describes the creature's mouth like this:

the lipless brim … quivered and panted, and dropped saliva.

a) What is the effect of this choice of words?

....

....

1 mark

b) Find and copy another example of language from the same paragraph that has a similar effect.

....

1 mark

32 In the paragraph starting 'Those who have never seen a living Martian…', what details suggest that the creature is not suited to living on earth?

....

....

1 mark

pages
14–15
total

please turn over

Revision Guide links
If you need help after your test has been marked, read the following pages in the Revision Guide:
Question 30 page 13   Question 31 page 12
Question 32 page 12

Schofield & Sims • Key Stage 2 **English Practice Papers**   15

33 The writer describes the Martian as 'at once vital, intense, inhuman, crippled and monstrous'.

Draw lines to match these words to their meaning.

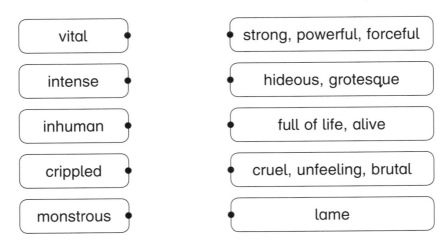

vital	strong, powerful, forceful
intense	hideous, grotesque
inhuman	full of life, alive
crippled	cruel, unfeeling, brutal
monstrous	lame

2 m

34 Which of the following would be the most suitable title to summarise the events in this extract?

Tick **one**.

The Martian's land ☐

A message from Mars ☐

The cylinder opens ☐

A crowd gathers ☐

1 m

Revision Guide links
If you need help after your test has been marked, read the following pages in the Revision Guide:
Question 33 page 4   Question 34 page 7

35 The tension builds throughout the extract.

Look at the paragraph beginning 'I think everyone expected to see a man...'.

Explain how this paragraph is important in helping to build that suspense. Explain fully, referring to events both within the paragraph and in the extract as a whole.

....

....

....

....

....

....

3 marks

36 Based on what you have read, what does the last paragraph suggest might happen next?

Use evidence from this paragraph to support your prediction.

....

....

....

....

....

2 marks

END OF TEST

pages
16–17
total

**Total score for
Reading Paper**
Write this score in the box
on pages 3 and 50.

Revision Guide links
If you need help after your test has been marked,
read the following pages in the Revision Guide:
Question 35 page 11   Question 36 page 6

Instructions for the Grammar, Punctuation and Spelling test

The Key Stage 2 Grammar, Punctuation and Spelling test is split into two papers. These papers should be done in this order.

Grammar, Punctuation and Spelling Paper 1: questions (pages 20–34)

Grammar, Punctuation and Spelling Paper 2: spelling (pages 35–36)

Instructions for Paper 1: questions

You have 45 minutes to answer the questions in Paper 1. There will be questions on grammar, punctuation and vocabulary.

You will find different types of question and you will need to answer these in different ways. Always read the instructions carefully so that you know how to answer each question. The space for your answer shows the type of answer you need to write.

Selected answers

For some questions you do not need to do any writing. You just need to select the right answer from those given. For example, you might need to tick the right answer, circle certain words, label or underline part of a sentence.

> **Note:** When answering these questions, make sure you only tick the required number of boxes or circle or underline the required words. You will not get the mark if you select any additional words.

Short answers

For some questions you need to write a word, a few words or a sentence. These questions have a line or a box for you to write your answer.

> **Note:** If you write a sentence, make sure it is punctuated correctly, beginning with a capital letter and with the right punctuation mark at the end. Do not use capital letters for words in the middle of sentences unless needed.

With questions involving contracted forms, plurals, verb tenses and prefixes and suffixes, correct spelling is generally required even on Paper 1. You cannot use a dictionary or spell checker.

Work through the paper until your time is up. Try to answer all of the questions. If you can't answer a question, move on to the next one and then go back to it later.

Work as quickly and as carefully as you can. If you finish before the time is up, go back and check your work.

You are now ready to start the practice paper. Remember, you have **45 minutes** to answer the questions.

Instructions for Paper 2: spelling

In this test you will have 20 words to spell. The test should take about 15 minutes to complete but it is not a timed test.

You cannot use a dictionary or a spell checker in this test.

You will need an adult to help you carry out the test. Before you start, the adult should remove the pull-out page containing the instructions and the words for the test (found before the answer section).

The adult who is helping you will read out 20 sentences. You will have the sentences in front of you. Each sentence will have a missing word. You should listen carefully to each missing word and write it in the space, making sure you spell it correctly.

If you make a mistake or want to change a spelling, cross it out and write the word again. Make sure it is clear which answer you want to be marked.

After you have finished all 20 questions, you will have a chance to hear the sentences again. Check your spellings and make any changes you wish.

> **Note for adults helping with Grammar, Punctuation and Spelling Paper 2: spelling**
> You should remove the spelling instructions (found before the answer section) before the child begins the test. This pull-out page provides more detailed instructions and the words for the test.

**DO NOT TURN OVER THIS PAGE UNTIL YOU ARE READY TO START
GRAMMAR, PUNCTUATION AND SPELLING PAPER 1**

Grammar, Punctuation and Spelling Paper 1: questions

1   Which sentence below is written in the **past tense**?

Tick **one**.

An otter lives in or near water. ☐

Otters are superb swimmers. ☐

The number of otters declined for a time. ☐

Otters have short legs with webbed toes. ☐

1 m

2   Tick the sentence that must end with an **exclamation mark**.

Tick **one**.

What happened ☐

What a success ☐

I know what to do ☐

Tell me what you want ☐

1 m

3   Write the **contracted form** of the underlined words in the box.

Yes, <u>we would</u> like to help.

↓

☐

1 mc

Revision Guide links
If you need help after your test has been
marked, read the following pages in the
Revision Guide:
Question 1 page 43   Question 2 page 36
Question 3 page 53

4 Draw a line to match each **prefix** to the correct word so that it makes a new verb.

Prefix	Word
de	approve
dis	cross
un	compose
mis	sleep
over	interpret

1 mark

5 Which pair of **verbs** correctly completes the sentence below?

These gardens _____ once overgrown and forgotten, but now they _____ a magnificent sight.

Tick **one**.

are   were   ☐

were   were   ☐

are   are   ☐

were   are   ☐

1 mark

6 Label the boxes with the correct letter to show the **word classes**.

A verb   **B** adverb   **C** noun   **D** adjective

This show sounds amazing. Perhaps we should book tickets.

1 mark

pages
20–21
total

Revision Guide links
If you need help after your test has been marked,
read the following pages in the Revision Guide:
Question 4 pages 5, 49   Question 5 page 43
Question 6 page 47

please turn over

7 Insert a **comma** in the correct place in the sentence below.

Still half asleep the children trooped down the stairs into the hall.

1 mark

8 Circle **one** word in each underlined pair to complete the sentences using **Standard English**.

The twins **was/were** going to wash the plates but I **did/done** it first.

Joe could **have/of** helped but he **wasn't/weren't** there.

1 mark

9 Tick **one** box in each row to show whether the sentence is a **command** or a **statement**.

Sentence	Statement	Command
I want you to help me wash up.		
First of all, collect the plates and dishes.		
Don't put them in the bowl yet.		
We need some hot water.		

1 mark

10 Circle all the **pronouns** in the sentence below.

She smiled at us as we helped ourselves to a second helping of her delicious pudding.

1 mark

Revision Guide links
If you need help after your test has been marked, read the following pages in the Revision Guide:
Question 7 page 51   Question 8 page 46
Question 9 page 36   Question 10 page 45

11 Complete the sentence below using **three** different **co-ordinating conjunctions**.

We could go to the cinema .... stay in .... watch television, ... it is too cold to play outside.

1 mark

12 Circle all the words in the sentence below that should start with a **capital letter**.

last may, eric fellows and his wife, jean, visited paris to see the eiffel tower.

1 mark

13 Add a question tag to make this sentence into a **question**. Remember to punctuate your answer correctly.

You will help me, ...

1 mark

14 What does the word 'it' refer to in the sentence below?

Jamie's plan was to use the milk to tempt the kitten out of the tree – but it didn't work.

Tick **one**.

the kitten ☐

the milk ☐

the plan ☐

the tree ☐

1 mark

pages 22–23 total

Revision Guide links
If you need help after your test has been marked, read the following pages in the Revision Guide:
Question 11 page 35   Question 12 page 50
Question 13 page 36   Question 14 page 45

please turn over

15 Which sentence uses the **apostrophe** correctly?

Tick **one**.

The womens belonging's were left on the train. ☐

The women's belongings were left on the train. ☐

The womens' belongings were left on the train. ☐

The womens belongings' were left on the train. ☐

1 ma

16 Circle all the **conjunctions** in the sentences below.

It was after nine o'clock when he arrived at the farm.

He smelt the smoke before he saw the flames.

As he ran into the yard, he saw the barn burning.

1 ma

17 Circle one word in each underlined pair to complete the sentences using **Standard English**.

Sam and **I/me** saw a fox over by **them/those** trees.

I'm sure it was a fox **that/what** we saw.

1 mar

Revision Guide links
If you need help after your test has been marked, read the following pages in the Revision Guide:
Question 15 page 53   Question 16 page 39
Question 17 page 46

18 Write a sentence that lists all the information given below. Remember to punctuate your answer correctly.

Items you need

waterproof coat

sensible shoes

rucksack

packed lunch (including a drink)

....

....

....

1 mark

19 Tick **one** box to show where a **full stop** is needed in the passage below.

That was the story Tom told Lucy and I listened but we did not really believe him.

1 mark

20 Write a sentence using the word <u>flat</u> as a **noun**. Remember to punctuate your answer correctly.

....

1 mark

21 Write a sentence using the word <u>flat</u> as an **adjective**. Remember to punctuate your answer correctly.

....

1 mark

pages
24–25
total

Revision Guide links
If you need help after your test has been marked,
read the following pages in the Revision Guide:
Question 18 page 51   Question 19 page 50
Question 20 page 47   Question 21 page 47

please turn over

22 Tick **one** box in each row to show how the **modal verb** affects the meaning of the sentence.

Sentence	Modal verb shows **certainty**	Modal verb shows **possibility**
It could rain today.		
I can be there by six o'clock.		
It will be too late to go to the library.		
Mark might come later.		

1 mc

23 Underline the part of the sentence that is a **relative clause**.

The little dog that lives next door always barks at me when I pass.

1 mc

24 Complete the sentence with a **possessive pronoun**.

Is that book ....?

1 m

25 Rewrite the sentence below as **direct speech**. Remember to punctuate your answer correctly.

Mrs James asked us if we would like to help.

Mrs James ....

1 mc

Revision Guide links
If you need help after your test has been marked, read the following pages in the Revision Guide:
Question 22 page 44   Question 23 page 40
Question 24 page 45   Question 25 page 52

26 What does the root <u>spect</u> mean in the word family below?

spectacles   inspect   spectator

Tick **one**.

wait ☐

look ☐

judge ☐

help ☐

1 mark

27 Tick **one** box in each row to show whether the underlined clause is a **main clause** or a **subordinate clause**.

Sentence	Main clause	Subordinate clause
Jack, <u>who was the captain of the team</u>, had a great game.		
The team equalised <u>after going behind in the first half.</u>		
<u>Everyone was relieved</u> when the final whistle blew.		

1 mark

28 Circle all the **prepositions** in the sentence below.

On his way home, the boy stopped and sat under a tree by the roadside, waiting until the sun began to set over the mountain.

1 mark

29 Circle the **two** words in the sentence below that are **antonyms** of each other.

I often visit the new leisure centre on Saturdays but I have rarely seen it this busy.

1 mark

pages 26–27 total

please turn over

Revision Guide links
If you need help after your test has been marked, read the following pages in the Revision Guide:
Question 26 page 5   Question 27 page 39
Question 28 page 47   Question 29 page 49

30 Rewrite the sentence below adding a **subordinate clause**. Remember to punctuate your answer correctly.

Kate was feeling miserable.

....

....

1 m

31 Tick the sentence that uses the **past progressive** verb form.

Tick **one**.

While Ruby waits by the gate, Priya races to the finish. ☐

While Ruby waited by the gate, Priya raced to the finish. ☐

While Ruby was waiting by the gate, Priya was racing to the finish. ☐

While Ruby was by the gate, Priya was already at the finish. ☐

1 m

32 Draw a line to match each word with its correct **synonym**.

Word	Synonym
enough	exclude
surprising	inefficient
wasteful	sufficient
omit	unexpected

1 mc

Revision Guide links
If you need help after your test has been marked, read the following pages in the Revision Guide:
Question 30 pages 39, 41
Question 31 page 43
Question 32 page 48

33 Complete the sentence with a **verb** formed from the noun shown in brackets.

His behaviour will .... you. [horror]

I must .... for my brother's behaviour. [apology]

1 mark

34 Which sentence is punctuated correctly?

Tick **one**.

I was hungry starving, in fact – so I took a cake from the tray. ☐

I was hungry – starving – in fact, so I took a cake from the tray. ☐

I was hungry – starving, in fact – so I took a cake from the tray. ☐

I was hungry – starving, in fact so I took a cake from the tray. ☐

1 mark

35 Tick **one** box in each row to show whether the underlined words are the **subject** or **object** of the sentence.

Sentence	Subject	Object
Harry painted <u>a picture</u>.		
<u>Cows</u> eat grass.		
My team won <u>the trophy</u>.		

1 mark

please turn over

Revision Guide links
If you need help after your test has been marked, read the following pages in the Revision Guide:
Question 33 page 5   Question 34 page 54
Question 35 pages 35, 44

36 Complete the table below by adding a **suffix** to each noun to make an **adjective**.

Noun	Adjective
home	
centre	
fur	
poison	
pity	

1 mark

37 Tick **one** box to show where a **dash** should go in the sentence below.

It began to rain as soon as we arrived at the campsite it was not a good start.

1 mark

38 Tick **all** the sentences that contain an **adverb**.

The coach should be here soon. ☐

It is often a little late. ☐

Let's go and wait outside. ☐

It is a lovely day for a trip. ☐

1 mark

Revision Guide links
If you need help after your test has been marked, read the following pages in the Revision Guide:
Question 36 pages 5, 60–61
Question 37 page 54
Question 38 page 37

39 Which sentence is written in the **active voice**?

Tick **one**.

The flight was delayed by the bad weather. ☐

The police carried out the investigation. ☐

The money was left on the counter. ☐

Two men were seen leaving the property. ☐

1 mark

40 Insert a pair of **brackets** in the correct place in the sentence below.

Then Max who had been standing right next to me disappeared in a cloud of smoke.

1 mark

41 Explain how the **comma** changes the meaning in the two sentences.

Grace, Thomas is here.

Grace Thomas is here.

....

....

....

....

1 mark

42 Rewrite the sentence below so that it is written in the **passive voice**. Remember to punctuate your answer correctly.

The children measured the plants every day.

....

1 mark

pages 30–31 total

please turn over

Revision Guide links
If you need help after your test has been marked, read the following pages in the Revision Guide:
Question 39 page 44   Question 40 page 54
Question 41 page 51   Question 42 page 44

43 Which punctuation mark should be used in the place indicated by the arrow?

The dessert comes in three flavours ⭡ strawberry, banana and chocolate.

Tick **one**.

a full stop ☐

a comma ☐

a colon ☐

a semi-colon ☐

1 mc

44 Tick **one** box in each row to show whether the word <u>since</u> is used as a **subordinating conjunction** or a **preposition**.

Sentence	<u>since</u> used as a **conjunction**	<u>since</u> used as a **preposition**
I have been waiting *since* 5 o'clock.		
Nothing has happened *since* we arrived.		
I will stay here *since* it is already quite late.		

1 me

45 Complete the sentence below so that it uses the **subjunctive form**.

If he .... here today, he would be delighted.

1 me

Revision Guide links
If you need help after your test has been marked, read the following pages in the Revision Guide:
Question 43 page 55   Question 44 page 47
Question 45 page 81

46 Circle all the **determiners** in the sentence below.

There weren't many biscuits left, but I found two chocolate chip cookies in the tin.

1 mark

47 Underline the longest possible **noun phrase** in the sentence below.

In the corner, one old man with a white beard was snoring contentedly.

1 mark

48 Which sentence is punctuated correctly?

Tick **one**.

Harvey is a long-haired-white rabbit. ☐

Harvey is a long, haired, white rabbit. ☐

Harvey is a long-haired white rabbit. ☐

Harvey is a long haired-white rabbit. ☐

1 mark

pages
32–33
total

Revision Guide links
If you need help after your test has been marked,
read the following pages in the Revision Guide:
Question 46 page 38   Question 47 page 38
Question 48 page 56

please turn over

49 Tick the sentence that uses the **present perfect** verb form.

Tick **one**.

We are hoping to raise lots of money. ☐

We have made a good start. ☐

We held a cake sale last week. ☐

It is hard work but also rewarding. ☐

1 mc

50 Which punctuation mark should be used in the place indicated by the arrow?

Marie immediately wanted to explore I just wanted to rest and take in the view.

↑

Tick **one**.

comma ☐

semi-colon ☐

exclamation mark ☐

hyphen ☐

1 mc

END OF TEST

page
tot

Total score for Grammar, Punctuation and Spelling Paper 1
Write this score in the box on pages 3 and 51.

Revision Guide links
If you need help after your test has been marked, read the following pages in the Revision Guide:
Question 49 page 43   Question 50 page 55

Grammar, Punctuation and Spelling Paper 2: spelling

The adult who is helping you will read out the sentences and tell you what words to write in the gaps. Listen carefully.

1   I hope you did not .... at school.

1 mark

2   The training .... left me quite exhausted.

1 mark

3   The .... in the mountains was stunning.

1 mark

4   There was no .... in my mind about the winner.

1 mark

5   Everyone's fingerprints are .... to them.

1 mark

6   I have nothing but .... for the losing team.

1 mark

7   It was an .... victory.

1 mark

8   Mum gave me a .... about tidying my room.

1 mark

9   Molly Jones is my next-door ....

1 mark

10 The man hiding in the shadows looked ....

1 mark

Revision Guide links
If you need help after your test has been marked,
read the following pages in the Revision Guide:

Question 1 page 5	Question 2 page 59
Question 3 page 62	Question 4 page 62
Question 5 page 62	Question 6 page 63
Question 7 page 59	Question 8 page 59
Question 9 page 63	Question 10 page 59

page 35 total

please turn over

11 It was a steep .... from the mountain top.

1 m

12 The party was a very special ....

1 m

13 Please don't .... me in front of my friends.

1 m

14 The .... tuned up before they began to play.

1 m

15 Her relief was .... to everyone.

1 m

16 It was .... hot today.

1 m

17 I was .... fed up with the situation.

1 m

18 I was .... to see what was in the box.

1 m

19 There was a .... coming from under the door.

1 m

20 You can't trust someone who is ....

1 m

END OF TEST

pag to

Total score for Grammar, Punctuation and Spelling Paper 2
Write this score in the box on pages 3 and 51.

Revision Guide links

If you need help after your test has been marked, read the following pages in the Revision Guide:

Question 11 page 65   Question 12 page 59
Question 13 page 64   Question 14 page 62
Question 15 page 59   Question 16 page 59
Question 17 page 57   Question 18 page 59
Question 19 page 65   Question 20 page 63

Script for Grammar, Punctuation and Spelling Paper 2
(for adult helper)

The spelling test should take about 15 minutes but it is not a timed test.

Before you start

Before you start the spelling test, remove this page from the book. This page gives you the script and instructions for carrying out the test.

Go through the instructions on page 19 to introduce the test. Explain that each of the sentences in the practice paper has a missing word and that you will read out the sentences and say the missing word so the child can write it in the space.

When you are ready to start, tell the child to find the test on pages 35 and 36.

Carrying out the test

Check the child understands what to do and then begin the test.

Read the 20 spellings like this:

1. Give the spelling number: *Spelling 1*

2. Say: *The word is... misbehave*

3. Read the full sentence: *I hope you did not misbehave at school.*

4. Repeat: *The word is... misbehave*

Leave at least 12 seconds between spellings. You can repeat the target word if necessary.

After question 20, read all 20 sentences again so the child can check their spellings and make any changes.

continued overleaf

1. I hope you did not <u>misbehave</u> at school.

2. The training <u>session</u> left me quite exhausted.

3. The <u>scenery</u> in the mountains was stunning.

4. There was no <u>doubt</u> in my mind about the winner.

5. Everyone's fingerprints are <u>unique</u> to them.

6. I have nothing but <u>sympathy</u> for the losing team.

7. It was an <u>incredible</u> victory.

8. Mum gave me a <u>lecture</u> about tidying my room.

9. Molly Jones is my next-door <u>neighbour</u>.

10. The man hiding in the shadows looked <u>suspicious</u>.

11. It was a steep <u>descent</u> from the mountain top.

12. The party was a very special <u>occasion</u>.

13. Please don't <u>embarrass</u> me in front of my friends.

14. The <u>orchestra</u> tuned up before they began to play.

15. Her relief was <u>apparent</u> to everyone.

16. It was <u>uncomfortably</u> hot today.

17. I was <u>thoroughly</u> fed up with the situation.

18. I was <u>curious</u> to see what was in the box.

19. There was a <u>draught</u> coming from under the door.

20. You can't trust someone who is <u>deceitful</u>.

Answers and mark scheme

Reading Paper

Record the mark awarded for each question. Half marks cannot be awarded.

Question	Requirement	Marks
1	Award **1 mark** for identifying **three** of the following. • [soft] rains • [shimmering sound of] swallows • frogs [singing at night] • robins [whistling]	1 mark
2	Award **1 mark** for answers that refer to both the alliteration and the mood it creates, for example: • the soft whispering sounds create a sense of peacefulness • 'swallows circling' and 'shimmering sound' make soft, soothing, gentle sounds	1 mark
3	Award **1 mark** for answers that refer to the focus **both** before **and** after this point. **Before**: focus on beauty of nature, peacefulness **After**: focus on war, mankind's self-destruction	1 mark
4	Award **1 mark** for the correct option ticked. completely ☑	1 mark
5	Award **1 mark** for reference to mankind having destroyed itself with war, for example: because we (mankind) will all have died in the war	1 mark
6	Award **1 mark** for the correct option ticked. Nature will outlive the destruction of mankind ☑	1 mark
7	Award **2 marks** for answers that refer to **two** different interpretations that fit the poem (a literal and an inferred meaning), for example: • light rain like a shower, not heavy • quiet and gentle • soothing, calming Accept also references to positive effects of the rain, such as bringing life; pleasant.	2 marks
8	Award **2 marks** for **all four** correct. Award **1 mark** for **three** correct.	2 marks
9	Award **1 mark** for reference to any of the following acceptable points, up to a maximum of **2 marks**. • they are extinct/no-one's seen one • the pictures of them looked different • the skeleton could not tell us everything	2 marks

Question	Requirement	Marks
10	Award **1 mark** for answers that refer to the sailors introducing new species to the island, for example: • new predators appeared such as pigs, rats, cats • their natural habitat was destroyed/their eggs were eaten by the new animals the sailors brought with them	1 mark
11	Award **2 marks** for an answer that refers to at least **two** pieces of relevant information: • flightless; couldn't fly away • unguarded; not used to predators so it didn't recognise danger • its nest was on the ground so exposed/easy to reach Award **1 mark** for one piece of relevant information.	2 marks
12	Award **1 mark** for a suitable synonym, for example: strange/weird/peculiar	1 mark
13	Award **1 mark** for **all four** correct.	1 mark

	True	False
The dodo only ever lived on the island of Mauritius.	✓	
There is no scientific evidence that dodos existed.		✓
There are no records of dodos before 1598.	✓	
Savery's painting of a dodo was entirely accurate.		✓

Question	Requirement	Marks
14	Award **1 mark** for reference to any of the following acceptable points from the introduction: • a haven for wildlife • escape the hustle and bustle • a calming walk	1 mark
15	Award **1 mark** for identifying any **two** of the following points mentioned in the information leaflet: • pick flowers • take wildlife/animals/creatures away • leave litter • let their dogs damage the woods	1 mark
16	Award **1 mark** for a definition from the text: woods that have existed since at least the sixteenth century	1 mark
17	Award **1 mark** for answers that explain how it let in more sunlight, which encouraged a greater range of plants to grow and so more wildlife. **Do not** accept answers that only mention letting in more sunlight.	1 mark
18	Award **1 mark** for **all four** correct.	1 mark

	Fact	Opinion
A walk in the woods is always pleasant.		✓
The woods are close to the town of Tenbury.	✓	
The woods are a Local Nature Reserve.	✓	
The woods are special.		✓

Question	Requirement	Marks
19	Award **1 mark** for reference to any of the following acceptable points, up to a maximum of **2 marks**. • accessible – close to car park • flat, well-made path • easy/not strenuous – a stroll • there are benches to rest	2 marks
20	Award **1 mark** for identifying any **two** of the following activities. • bird-watching [in the hide]/spotting birds • attend an art or craft class/look for woodland sculptures • visit the exhibition in the Visitor Centre Accept also: crossing the stream via stepping stones.	1 mark
21	Award **1 mark** for **all four** pairs matched correctly. spring ⟍ finding fungi summer ⟍⟋ dramatic photographs autumn ⟋⟍ seeing a kingfisher winter ⟋ bird-watching	1 mark
22	Award **2 marks** for answers that contain **both** an appropriate reference to the positive attitude, inferred from the text, **and** an explanation in the form of a relevant quote and/or example(s), for example: **Positive attitude**, e.g. he feels lucky/fortunate; happy/pleased; excited/enthusiastic **Supporting quotes/examples**, such as: • the privilege of enjoying the beauty of Tenbury Woods every day • a stunning place to be; ever-changing little paradise • always something to see and do • enthusiasm for activities: taking photographs, sharing with visitors Award **1 mark** for **either** a positive attitude inferred from the text **or** giving a relevant quote.	2 marks
23	a Award **1 mark** for the correct option indicated. (grown)	1 mark
	b Award **1 mark** for the correct option indicated. (to get a better view)	1 mark
	c Award **1 mark** for the correct option indicated. (annoyed)	1 mark
24	Award **1 mark** for identifying **one** of the following points. • because it was being screwed out from within/the screw was moving from the inside • there was a humming sound	1 mark
25	Award **1 mark** for answers referring to hearing the sound of the lid falling on the gravel, such as: he heard it fall on the gravel **Do not** accept answers that just refer to the lid falling off or ones that say he saw the lid fall on the gravel.	1 mark

Question	Requirement	Marks
26	Award **1 mark** for the correct option indicated. earthly, of earth ☑	1 mark
27	Award **1 mark** for the correct answer. tentacles	1 mark
28	Award **1 mark** for identifying **all three** of the following words. writhing wriggled coiled	1 mark
29	a Award **1 mark** for answers that refer to the mood **both** before **and** after, for example: **Before**: excited/astonished/curious **After**: scared/terrified/horrified	1 mark
	b Award **1 mark** for answers that refer to the actions/reactions of **both** the crowd **and** the narrator, for example: the crowd screamed/backed off/ran away but the narrator stood still/was too gripped to move/stayed staring at it	1 mark
30	Award **1 mark** for explaining how a comparison uses something the reader will recognise, for example: • because we know how big bears are • we can picture its skin because we know what wet leather looks like	1 mark
31	a Award **1 mark** for answers referring to making it sound disgusting/revolting/repulsive/sickening	1 mark
	b Award **1 mark** for the following example: [the whole creature] heaved and pulsated convulsively Accept also: lank tentacular appendage.	1 mark
32	Award **1 mark** for reference to **either** acceptable point. • its [heavy] breathing in a strange atmosphere – the tumultuous breathing of the lungs • the heaviness and painfulness of movement in the earth's gravity	1 mark
33	Award **2 marks** for **all five** correctly matched. vital — full of life, alive intense — strong, powerful, forceful inhuman — cruel, unfeeling, brutal crippled — lame monstrous — hideous, grotesque Award **1 mark** for **three or four** correctly matched.	2 marks
34	Award **1 mark** for the correct option indicated. The cylinder opens ☑	1 mark

Question	Requirement	Marks
35	Award **3 marks** for answers that fully explain how events build suspense within the paragraph **and** how it contributes to the extract as a whole, **both** supported by reference to the text. Example of points for extract as a whole: • it's been building up to the moment when we find out what is inside • it gives us the first glimpse of what is inside the spaceship • it changes the mood from excitement to horror Within the paragraph: • starts with what everyone expected to see and then describes what was actually inside • the first line suggests it won't be like a man at all and makes you wonder what it is like • at first everything is shadowy and unclear; then it becomes clearer; the creature is revealed slowly, first just shapes and its eyes; it's described so we're not sure what it is at first Award **2 marks** for answers that refer to suspense within the paragraph **and** the extract as a whole but which are not fully supported with reference to text. Award **1 mark** for less developed answers that show understanding of how suspense is developed within the paragraph **or** the extract as a whole.	3 marks
36	Award **2 marks** for an acceptable point that is also supported by text-based evidence. Award **1 mark** for **either** an acceptable point **or** a relevant piece of text-based evidence. Acceptable points (with evidence in brackets): • further encounters ('even at this first encounter') • something dreadful is going to happen; Martian will kill/attack people (reference to 'overcome with ... dread'); feeling of menace in description of Martian ('monstrous'; 'unspeakably nasty'; 'inhuman') • fear and terror will spread (the horror of its appearance; reaction of the narrator)	2 marks

Grammar, Punctuation and Spelling Paper 1: questions

Record the mark awarded for each question. Half marks cannot be awarded.

Question	Requirement	Marks
1	Award **1 mark** for the correct answer. The number of otters declined for a time. ☑	1 mark
2	Award **1 mark** for the correct answer. What a success ☑	1 mark
3	Award **1 mark** for the correct contracted form with the correct spelling and correct placement of the apostrophe. we'd	1 mark
4	Award **1 mark** for **all five** correct. de — cross dis — compose un — approve mis — interpret over — sleep	1 mark
5	Award **1 mark** for the correct answer. were are	1 mark
6	Award **1 mark** for **all four** correct. This show sounds amazing. Perhaps we should book tickets. C D B A	1 mark
7	Award **1 mark** for a correctly placed comma. Still half asleep, the children trooped down the stairs into the hall.	1 mark
8	Award **1 mark** for **all four** correct words circled. The twins was/(were) going to wash the plates but I (did)/done it first. Joe could (have)/of helped but he (wasn't)/weren't there.	1 mark
9	Award **1 mark** for a correctly completed table. <table><tr><th>Sentence</th><th>Statement</th><th>Command</th></tr><tr><td>I want you to help me wash up.</td><td>✓</td><td></td></tr><tr><td>First of all, collect the plates and dishes.</td><td></td><td>✓</td></tr><tr><td>Don't put them in the bowl yet.</td><td></td><td>✓</td></tr><tr><td>We need some hot water.</td><td>✓</td><td></td></tr></table>	1 mark
10	Award **1 mark** for **all** words correctly identified. (She) smiled at (us) as (we) helped (ourselves) to a second helping of (her) delicious pudding.	1 mark
11	Award **1 mark** for **all three** conjunctions correctly added. **Note**: Using a subordinating conjunction (such as 'because') or another word (like 'to') is **not** acceptable. We could go to the cinema **or** stay in **and** watch television, **but** it is too cold to play outside.	1 mark

Question	Requirement	Marks
12	Award **1 mark** for **all** words correctly identified. (last) (may) (eric) (fellows) and his wife, (jean) visited (paris) to see the (eiffel) (tower).	1 mark
13	Award **1 mark** for a correct question tag with the correct spelling and correct use of an apostrophe and question mark. You will help me, <u>won't you</u>?	1 mark
14	Award **1 mark** for the correct answer. the plan ☑	1 mark
15	Award **1 mark** for the correct answer. The women's belongings were left on the train. ☑	1 mark
16	Award **1 mark** for **all three** conjunctions identified. **Do not** award the mark if additional words are also circled. It was after nine o'clock (when) he arrived at the farm. He smelt the smoke (before) he saw the flames. (As) he ran into the yard, he saw the barn burning.	1 mark
17	Award **1 mark** for **all three** correct words circled. Sam and (I)/me saw a fox over by them/(those) trees. I'm sure it was a fox (that)/what we saw.	1 mark
18	Award **1 mark** for a correctly punctuated sentence, for example: You will need a waterproof coat, sensible shoes, a rucksack and a packed lunch (including a drink). Responses that use a colon after a suitable introductory clause are also acceptable, for example: You will need the following items: a waterproof coat, sensible shoes, a rucksack and a packed lunch (including a drink).	1 mark
19	Award **1 mark** for full stop in correct position. That was the story Tom told**.** Lucy and I listened but we did not really believe him.	1 mark
20	Award **1 mark** for a grammatically correct sentence that uses <u>flat</u> as a noun and is correctly punctuated, for example: I live in a first floor flat.	1 mark
21	Award **1 mark** for a grammatically correct sentence that uses <u>flat</u> as an adjective and is correctly punctuated, for example: My house has a flat roof.	1 mark
22	Award **1 mark** for a correctly completed table.	1 mark
23	Award **1 mark** for the correct part of the sentence underlined. The little dog <u>that lives next door</u> always barks at me when I pass.	1 mark

Table for Question 22:

Sentence	Certainty	Possibility
It could rain today.		✓
I can be there by six o'clock.	✓	
It will be too late to go to the library.	✓	
Mark might come later.		✓

Question	Requirement	Marks
24	Award **1 mark** for a suitable possessive pronoun. mine, yours, his, hers	1 mark
25	Award **1 mark** for a correctly punctuated response. Mrs James asked, "Would you like to help?"	1 mark
26	Award **1 mark** for the correct answer. look ☑	1 mark
27	Award **1 mark** for a correctly completed table. 	Sentence	Main clause	Subordinate clause
Jack, <u>who was the captain of the team</u>, had a great game.		✓
The team equalised <u>after going behind in the first half</u>.		✓
<u>Everyone was relieved</u> when the final whistle blew.	✓			1 mark
28	Award **1 mark** for **all four** correct words circled. No other words should be circled. (On) his way home, the boy stopped and sat (under) a tree (by) the roadside, waiting until the sun began to set (over) the mountain.	1 mark
29	Award **1 mark** for **both** correct words circled. I (often) visit the new leisure centre on Saturdays but I have (rarely) seen it this busy.	1 mark
30	Award **1 mark** for a sentence containing a subordinate clause with correct punctuation, for example: Kate was feeling miserable even though it was her birthday. Kate was feeling miserable because she had a bad cold. As she watched the rain falling, Kate was feeling miserable. **Do not** accept an answer if it uses a phrase instead of a subordinate clause or adds another main clause.	1 mark
31	Award **1 mark** for the correct answer. While Ruby was waiting by the gate, Priya was racing to the finish.	1 mark
32	Award **1 mark** for **all four** correct. enough — exclude surprising — inefficient wasteful — sufficient omit — unexpected	1 mark
33	Award **1 mark** for the correct words with the correct spelling. horrify/apologise	1 mark
34	Award **1 mark** for the correct answer. I was hungry – starving, in fact – so I took a cake from the tray. ☑	1 mark

Question	Requirement	Marks
35	Award **1 mark** for a correctly completed table. 	Sentence	Subject	Object
Harry painted <u>a picture</u>.		✓
<u>Cows</u> eat grass.	✓	
My team won <u>the trophy</u>.		✓		1 mark
36	Award **1 mark** for a correctly completed table with all words spelt correctly. Accept other appropriate adjectives as well as those shown. | Noun	Adjective
---	---
home	homeless, homely
centre	central
fur	furry
poison	poisonous
pity	pitiful, pitiless, piteous		1 mark
37	Award **1 mark** for the correct answer. It began to rain as soon as we arrived at the campsite it was not a good start. ↑ ✓	1 mark
38	Award **1 mark** for **all three** sentences correctly ticked. The coach should be here soon. ✓ It is often a little late. ✓ Let's go and wait outside. ✓	1 mark
39	Award **1 mark** for the correct answer. The police carried out the investigation. ✓	1 mark
40	Award **1 mark** for correctly placed brackets. Then Max (who had been standing right next to me) disappeared in a cloud of smoke.	1 mark
41	Award **1 mark** for an explanation of the meaning of **both** sentences, for example: The comma in the first sentence means someone is telling Grace that Thomas is here. There is no comma in the second sentence so it means that someone called Grace Thomas is here.	1 mark
42	Award **1 mark** for a sentence using the passive voice, for example: The plants were measured every day. The plants were measured by the children every day.	1 mark
43	Award **1 mark** for the correct answer. a colon ✓	1 mark

Question	Requirement	Marks
44	Award **1 mark** for a correctly completed table. | Sentence	Conjunction	Preposition | |---|---|---| | I have been waiting since 5 o'clock. | | ✓ | | Nothing has happened since we arrived. | ✓ | | | I will stay here since it is already quite late. | ✓ | |	1 mark
45	Award **1 mark** for use of the subjunctive form. were	1 mark
46	Award **1 mark** for **all** the correct words circled. There weren't (many) biscuits left, but I found (two) chocolate chip cookies in (the) tin.	1 mark
47	Award **1 mark** if **only** the full noun phrase is underlined. In the corner, <u>one old man with a white beard</u> was snoring contentedly.	1 mark
48	Award **1 mark** for the correct answer. Harvey is a long-haired white rabbit. ✓	1 mark
49	Award **1 mark** for the correct answer. We have made a good start. ✓	1 mark
50	Award **1 mark** for the correct answer. semi-colon ✓	1 mark

Grammar, Punctuation and Spelling Paper 2: spelling

Record the mark awarded for each question. Half marks cannot be awarded.

Question	Spelling	Marks	What is being tested?
1	misbehave	1 mark	Prefixes
2	session	1 mark	Endings which sound like 'shun': –tion, –sion, –ssion, –cian
3	scenery	1 mark	Words with the / s / sound spelt 'sc'
4	doubt	1 mark	Words with 'silent' letters
5	unique	1 mark	Words ending with the / g / sound spelt 'gue' or / k / sound spelt 'que'
6	sympathy	1 mark	The / i / sound spelt 'y' other than at the end of words
7	incredible	1 mark	Words ending in –able and –ible
8	lecture	1 mark	Words with endings –ture and –sure
9	neighbour	1 mark	Words with the / ay / sound spelt 'ei', 'eigh', or 'ey'
10	suspicious	1 mark	Endings which are spelt –cious or –tious
11	descent	1 mark	Homophones, near homophones and other words that are often confused
12	occasion	1 mark	Words ending in –sion
13	embarrass	1 mark	Common exception words
14	orchestra	1 mark	Words with a / k / sound spelt 'ch'
15	apparent	1 mark	Words ending in –ant, –ance, –ancy, –ent, –ence, –ency
16	uncomfortably	1 mark	Words ending in –ably and –ibly
17	thoroughly	1 mark	Words containing the letter-string 'ough'
18	curious	1 mark	The suffix –ous
19	draught	1 mark	Homophones, near homophones and other words that are often confused
20	deceitful	1 mark	Words with the / ee / sound spelt 'ei' after c

Total marks

Find the total marks of all the tests and write them in the boxes.

Total marks for Reading (out of 50)

What your Reading score means

Above 40 You are already achieving a good score and have good comprehension skills. There are still a few things you need to work on. Have a look at the questions you answered incorrectly. See if you can work out where you can get extra marks.

30–40 You already have the basic comprehension skills and can do many of the things expected of you but there are still some key areas you need to work on. Look at the Revision Guide links for the questions you answered incorrectly. This will show you the things you need to revise.

Below 30 You can do some of the things expected of you but there are still a number of areas you need to work on to help you understand fiction, poetry and non-fiction texts like those in the test. Ask an adult to help you revise the topics that you found difficult.

Revision Guide links

The Schofield & Sims **Key Stage 2 English Revision Guide** can help you with revising all the things you need to work on. It covers fiction, non-fiction and poetry, and includes guidance on reading for meaning and finding information. There are also Test Yourself questions and a helpful glossary where you can look up any words that you didn't understand in the practice papers.

Grammar, Punctuation and Spelling
Paper 1: questions (marks out of 50)

Grammar, Punctuation and Spelling
Paper 2: spelling (marks out of 20)

**Total marks for Grammar,
Punctuation and Spelling (out of 70)**

What your Grammar, Punctuation and Spelling score means

Above 56 You are already familiar with most of the aspects of spelling, grammar, punctuation and vocabulary that are tested at the end of Key Stage 2. There are still a few things you need to work on. Have a look at the questions you answered incorrectly. See if you can work out where you can get extra marks.

42–56 You recognise much of the grammar, punctuation and vocabulary being tested and can spell many words but there are still some key areas you need to work on. Look at the Revision Guide links for the questions you answered incorrectly. This will show you which areas of grammar and punctuation you need to revise and which spelling patterns you need to work on.

Below 42 You can do some of the things expected of you but there are still a number of areas you need to work on to answer questions and spell words like those in the test. Ask an adult to help you revise the topics that you found difficult.

Revision Guide links

The **Key Stage 2 English Revision Guide** covers all the grammar, punctuation and spelling topics, and can help you with revising all the things you need to work on. There are Test Yourself questions and a helpful glossary where you can look up any words that you didn't understand in the practice papers.

Schofield & Sims

the long-established educational publisher specialising in maths, English and science

The **Key Stage 2 English Practice Papers** contained in this book reflect the appearance and content of the national tests at Key Stage 2. Papers on reading, grammar, punctuation and spelling are included, as well as full instructions and detailed mark schemes. Cross-references to the separate **Key Stage 2 English Revision Guide** allow children and adult helpers to tailor revision for exam success.

The Schofield & Sims **Practice Papers** are closely matched to the National Curriculum test frameworks and help children to revise what they have learnt at school, in preparation for the end of key stage tests. Detailed instructions on using the papers, and guidance on equipment and timings, provide reassurance and help children to become familiar with a more formal test situation.

Five Schofield & Sims **Practice Papers** books are available, providing rigorous practice in maths and English at Key Stages 1 and 2, as well as science at Key Stage 2.

The **Practice Papers** feature:

- formal exam-style questions, similar to those found in the national tests
- comprehensive instructions for both the child and adult helper
- a clear mark scheme with additional comments and guidance
- cross-references to relevant information in the corresponding revision guide.

Key Stage 2 Maths
Revision Guide
ISBN 978 07217 1361 8

Key Stage 2 English
Revision Guide
ISBN 978 07217 1365 6

Key Stage 2 Science
Revision Guide
ISBN 978 07217 1369 4

Key Stage 2 Maths
Practice Papers
ISBN 978 07217 1363 2

Key Stage 2 English
Practice Papers
ISBN 978 07217 1367 0

Key Stage 2 Science
Practice Papers
ISBN 978 07217 1370 0

MIX
Paper from
responsible sources
FSC® C023114

ISBN 978-07217-1367-0

9 780721 713670

For further information and to place your order visit
www.schofieldandsims.co.uk or telephone 01484 607080

ISBN 978 07217 1367 0
Key Stage 2
Age range 7–11 years
£3.95 (Retail price)